# Time Pieces for Flute

## VOLUME 2

Arranged by Ian Denley

**ABRSM**

# CONTENTS

Published by ABRSM (Publishing) Ltd, a wholly owned subsidiary of ABRSM
© 1998 by The Associated Board of the Royal Schools of Music

# Time Pieces for Flute

## Volume 2

*for Christopher, David, Daniel and Peter*

## 1547 Que je chatoulle ta fossette

from *Danseries*, 2nd series

Pierre Attaingnant
(*c.*1494–1552)

# 1641 Kyrie Eleison

Claudio Monteverdi
(1567–1643)

AB 2672

poco rit.

# *c.*1655 **Menuet**

Louis Couperin
(*c.*1626–1661)

# 1700 The Catherine—A Country Dance

John Barrett
*(c.1676–c.1719)*

# 1730 Air
### HWV 425

George Frideric Handel
(1685–1759)

AB 2672

# 1766 Allegretto
K. 33b

# 1781 Variation VI

from *Serenade*, K. 361

Wolfgang Amadeus Mozart
(1756–1791)

# 1789 The Lass of Richmond Hill

James Hook
(1746–1827)

# *c.*1790 **Moderato**
from Sonatina in G

17/11/22

attrib. Ludwig van Beethoven
(1770–1827)

# 1818 Marche Militaire
### D. 733

Franz Schubert
(1797–1828)

# c.1823 Sentimental Waltz No. 5

from D. 779

Franz Schubert
(1797–1828)

# 1841 Villanelle

from *Les Nuits d'Eté*

Hector Berlioz
(1803–1869)

**Allegretto** ($\quarternote$ = *c.*112)

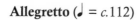

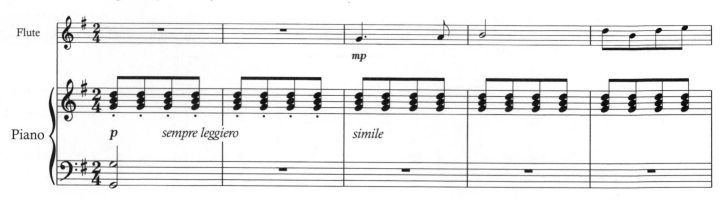

AB 2672

# 1878 Song without words

Op. 40 No. 6

Pyotr Tchaikovsky
(1840–1893)

**Allegro moderato** ($\quad$ = *c.*100)

# 1883 España

Emmanuel Chabrier
(1841–1894)

**Allegro giocoso** ($\downarrow. = c.60$)

Flute

Piano

# 1896 Are they gone now?
from *La Bohème*

Giacomo Puccini
(1858–1924)

AB 2672

# 1910 The Peace of Evening

from *Pelléas et Mélisande*

Jean Sibelius
(1865–1957)

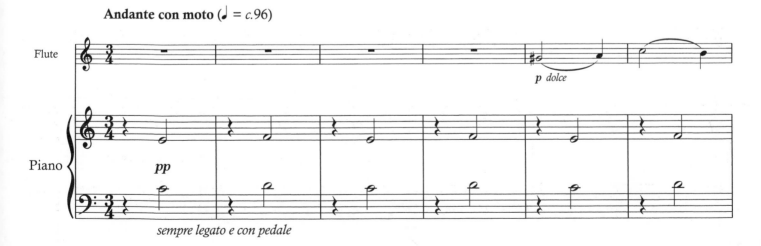

un poco piu mosso

# 1913 Prélude

Maurice Ravel
(1875–1937)

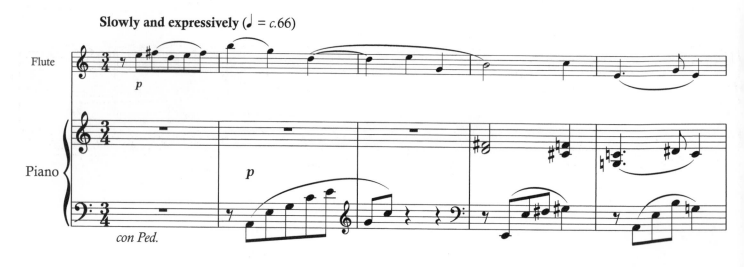

# 1965 Hurdy-Gurdy
from *Dances of the Dolls*

Dmitri Shostakovich
(1906–1975)

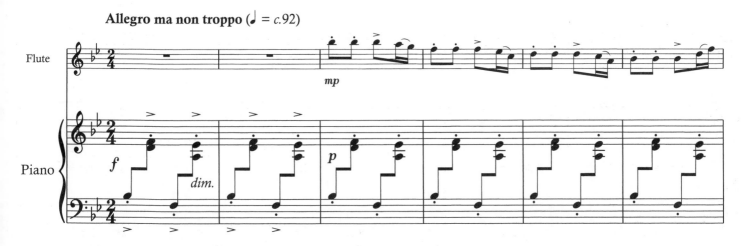

Reproduced and printed by
Halstan & Co. Ltd., Amersham, Bucks., England

Music origination by
Barnes Music Engraving Ltd, East Sussex